EZ,MH

E2, MH

THE ATTACK ON
PEARL HARBOR

BY CHRIS BOWMAN

ILLUSTRATION BY JOEL VOLLMER

COLOR BY GERARDO SANDOVAL

BELLWETHER MEDIA · MINNEAPOLIS, MN

STRAY FROM REGULAR READS
WITH BLACK SHEEP BOOKS.
FEEL A RUSH WITH EVERY READ!

Library of Congress Cataloging-in-Publication Data

Bowman, Chris, 1990-
    The Attack on Pearl Harbor / by Chris Bowman.
        pages cm. -- (Black Sheep: Disaster Stories)
    Includes bibliographical references and index.
    Summary: "Exciting illustrations follow the events of the attack on Pearl Harbor. The combination of brightly colored panels and leveled text is intended for students in grades 3 through 7"-- Provided by publisher.
    ISBN 978-1-62617-150-3 (hardcover : alkaline paper)
    1. Pearl Harbor (Hawaii), Attack on, 1941--Juvenile literature. I. Title.
    D767.92.B67 2014
    940.54'26693--dc23
                                   2014009036

This edition first published in 2015 by Bellwether Media, Inc.

Printed in the United States of America, North Mankato, MN.

TABLE OF CONTENTS

A Quiet Morning   4

Tensions Rising   6

Attack!   10

The Aftermath   18

More About the Disaster   22

Glossary   23

To Learn More   24

Index   24

Red text identifies
historical quotes.

A Quiet Morning

December 7, 1941:
It is a typical Sunday morning at Pearl Harbor. Sailors **stationed** at this Navy base on Oahu, Hawaii enjoy the day's relaxed rules.

Some use this time to catch up on sleep.

TENSIONS RISING

Admiral Nagano, this attack is necessary?

The relationship between the U.S. and Japan had been tense for years. In the 1930s, Japan tried to **conquer** China. Then they became an **Axis power** with Germany.

This worried the U.S. However, Americans **protested** war. Instead of fighting, the U.S. tried an **embargo**. They stopped sending oil and other resources to Japan.

Yes, Emperor Hirohito. It is the only way.

Japan needed oil to survive. Leaders decided to **invade** Southeast Asia to get their hands on it. But they knew this would anger the U.S. So they decided to attack the U.S. first.

The U.S. had no idea Pearl Harbor was a target. The base is about 4,000 miles from Japan. The Japanese military also appeared to be busy in Asia.

I wonder where the chow truck is? I'm so hungry!

7:02 a.m.
Army Privates George Elliot and Joseph Lockard are watching **radar** at Opana Point, Oahu. They detect the approaching Japanese planes.

Me, too. Hey, what is this? Are these planes?

Let me see that.

7:02 a.m.
Private Lockard warns Lieutenant Kermit Tyler at the information center. But Lieutenant Tyler assumes the planes are just American B-17s returning from a **recon mission**.

Large number of planes coming in from the north, three points east.

Don't worry about it.

The Japanese pilots listen to the Honolulu weather report as they fly toward Pearl Harbor. It says: *Clouds mostly over the mountains. Visibility good.*

We are approaching the island.

What do you see?

Those planes are flying awfully low.

A long white line of coast.

The Navy must be practicing dive-bombing again.

The USS *Oklahoma* meets a similar fate.

More than 400 sailors go down with the battleship.

Meanwhile, Honolulu is also in trouble. Japanese bombers only target the base. However, some U.S. anti-aircraft guns accidentally fire toward the city.

This way!

I've got you!

THE AFTERMATH

9:45 a.m.
The attack on Pearl Harbor is finally over.

2,403 Americans were killed in the attack. Another 1,178 were wounded.

188 planes were destroyed. 159 were damaged.

21 ships were sunk or damaged.

Luckily, the Navy's aircraft carriers were at sea during the attack.

On the other side, Japan lost only 29 aircraft and 5 small submarines.

Admiral Yamomoto, is something wrong? We were victorious!

I fear all we have done today is awaken a great, sleeping giant.

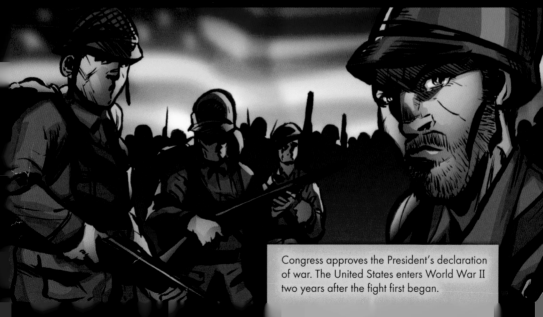

MORE ABOUT THE DISASTER

- To avoid being seen, the Japanese ships crossed the northern Pacific Ocean instead of major shipping routes.

- The "long white line of coast" seen by Japanese pilots refers to Oahu's Kakuku Point.

- *Tora! Tora! Tora!* means "Tiger! Tiger! Tiger!" in Japanese. It was the code word that meant they had surprised the U.S.

- The radar station that detected the Japanese planes was fairly new. It had been in operation for less than one month before the attacks.

- One of the U.S. Navy's aircraft carriers, USS *Enterprise*, was supposed to be in Pearl Harbor on the morning of the attack. However, rough seas delayed its arrival until after the attacks.

Glossary

ammunition–bullets or shells that can be shot

anti-aircraft guns–weapons fired at aircraft from the ground or sea

Axis power–a country that fought against the United States in World War II; the Axis powers were Germany, Japan, and Italy.

conquer–to take over by force

deck–a level of a ship or other vessel

depth charges–bombs dropped by ships that explode underwater at a certain depth; depth charges are used to attack submarines.

embargo–a ban on trade with another country

infamy–being well-known for a bad quality or act

invade–to enter a country by force to take control

periscope–an instrument on a submarine used to see above water

protested–publicly disagreed with something

radar–a system used to detect and track planes, ships, and other objects

recon mission–a secret mission used to gather information about an enemy

stationed–assigned to a specific place

To Learn More

AT THE LIBRARY

Lassieur, Allison. *The Attack on Pearl Harbor: An Interactive History Adventure*. Mankato, Minn.: Capstone Press, 2009.

Lemke, Donald. *Captured Off Guard: The Attack on Pearl Harbor*. Minneapolis, Minn.: Stone Arch Books, 2008.

White, Steve. *Day of Infamy: Attack on Pearl Harbor*. New York, N.Y.: Osprey, 2007.

ON THE WEB

Learning more about the attack on Pearl Harbor is as easy as 1, 2, 3.

1. Go to www.factsurfer.com.
2. Enter "attack on Pearl Harbor" into the search box.
3. Click the "Surf" button and you will see a list of related web sites.

With factsurfer.com, finding more information is just a click away.

Index

aircraft carriers, 13, 18
battleships, 13, 14, 15, 17
December 7, 1941, 4, 20
Elliot, George (private), 9
Fuchida, Mitsuo (commander), 10, 13
Hirohito (emperor), 6
historical quotes, 8, 9, 10, 11, 20, 21
Honolulu, Hawaii, 9, 15

Lockard, Joseph (private), 9
Nagano, Osami (admiral), 6
Ramsey, Logan C. (commander), 11
Roosevelt, Franklin D. (president), 20, 21
submarines, 8, 11, 19
Tyler, Kermit (lieutenant), 9
USS *Ward*, 8
Yamamoto, Isoroku (admiral), 19